1. The Ancient Egyptians

Religion was very important to the Ancient Egyptians. This priest is offering food and vases of
water to the falcon-headed sun god Ra-Horakhty. The Egyptian writing is a prayer.

2. The land of Egypt

Egypt is a hot country and a lot of it is desert. Here, papyrus plants are growing at the edge of the valley beside a tomb. The cow is an image of the goddess Hathor, who lived in the desert.

3. Growing food

The only fertile ground in Egypt is beside the river Nile. In this picture the Egyptian artist has drawn the river water flowing in canals all round the farmer's fields. The farmer in the top picture is cutting corn with a sickle. In the bottom picture he is ploughing with oxen.

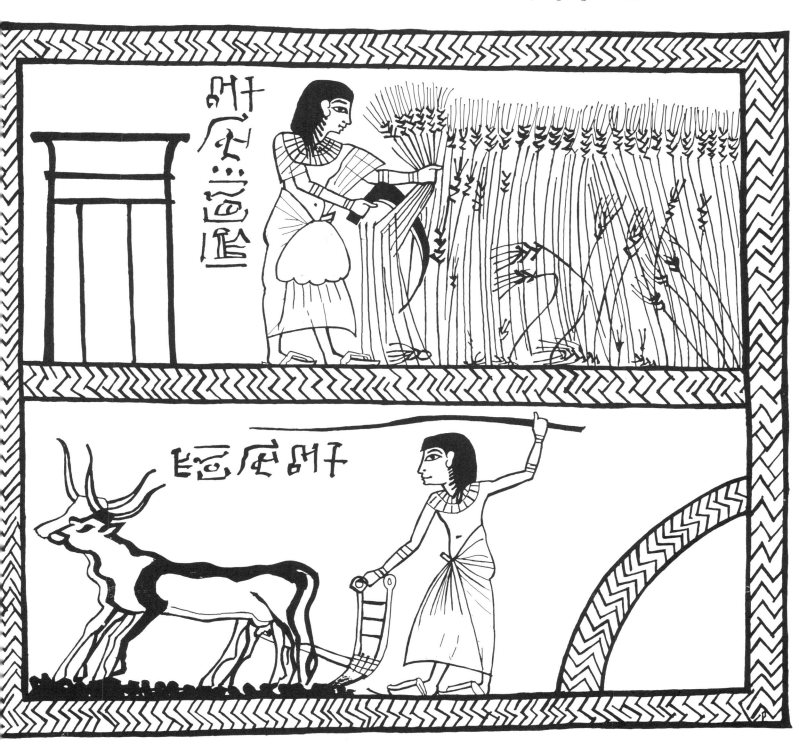

4. The king and queen

The king, or pharaoh, was the most important person in Ancient Egypt, almost a god. This king
and queen wear rich clothes and crowns.

5. The king in battle
King Ramses the Great captures an enemy in war.

6. The family

Family life was important. This picture of a mother, father and two children was carved on a tomb. The children's names are written in hieroglyphs. The girl's name is Neferhotephathor and the boy's is Nisuredy.

7. A party

This husband and wife are dressed up for a party. They both wear jewellery and wigs. He is smelling a lotus flower. The servant girl is bringing them wine. The things on their heads are lumps of perfumed ointment which slowly melt in the heat and make a pleasant scent. It must have been very messy.

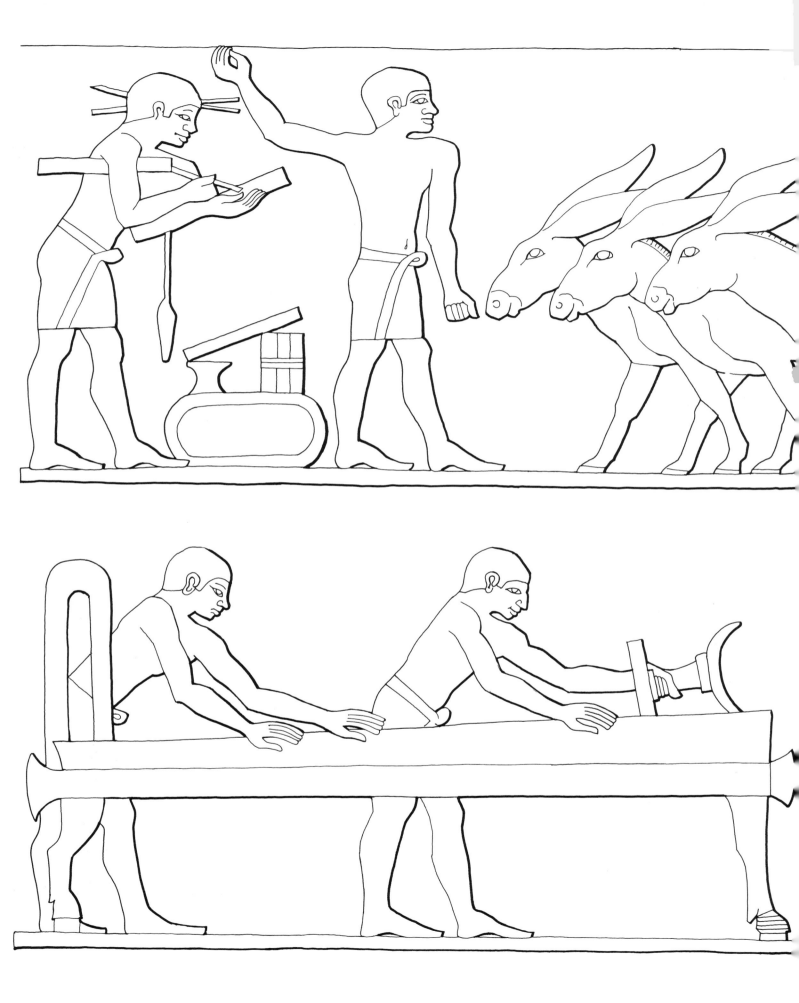

8. Everyday jobs

Rich Egyptians had servants to do all the work on their farms and in their houses. In the top picture a servant is driving donkeys towards a scribe who is writing down how many donkeys there are. Below, two servants are making a bed while others bring clean sheets. The bed has a wooden headrest instead of a pillow.

Scenes of everyday life like this were often carved or painted in rich people's tombs.

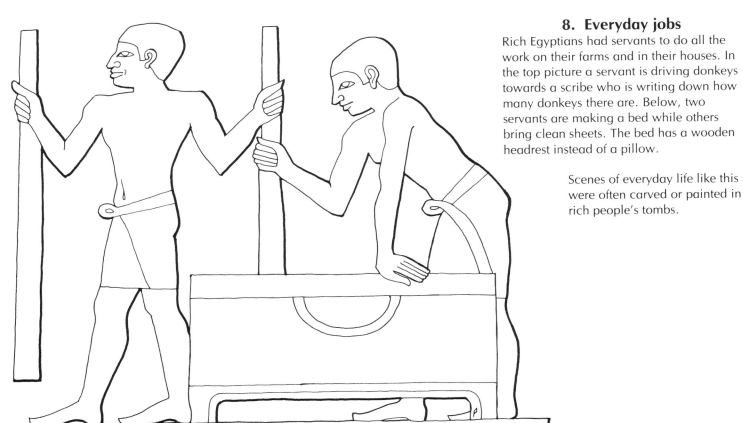

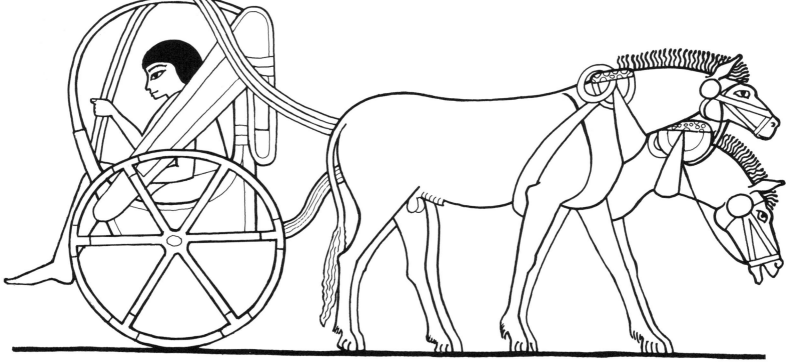

9. Chariots
The Ancient Egyptians used horses and mules to pull their chariots. These two servants are waiting for their masters to go for a ride.

10. A game

Sometimes the Egyptians painted animals in a comical way, doing human things. This lion and antelope come from a painting on a papyrus roll. They are playing *senet*, a board game which was popular in Ancient Egypt (and which people can still play today). The lion looks as if he's winning.

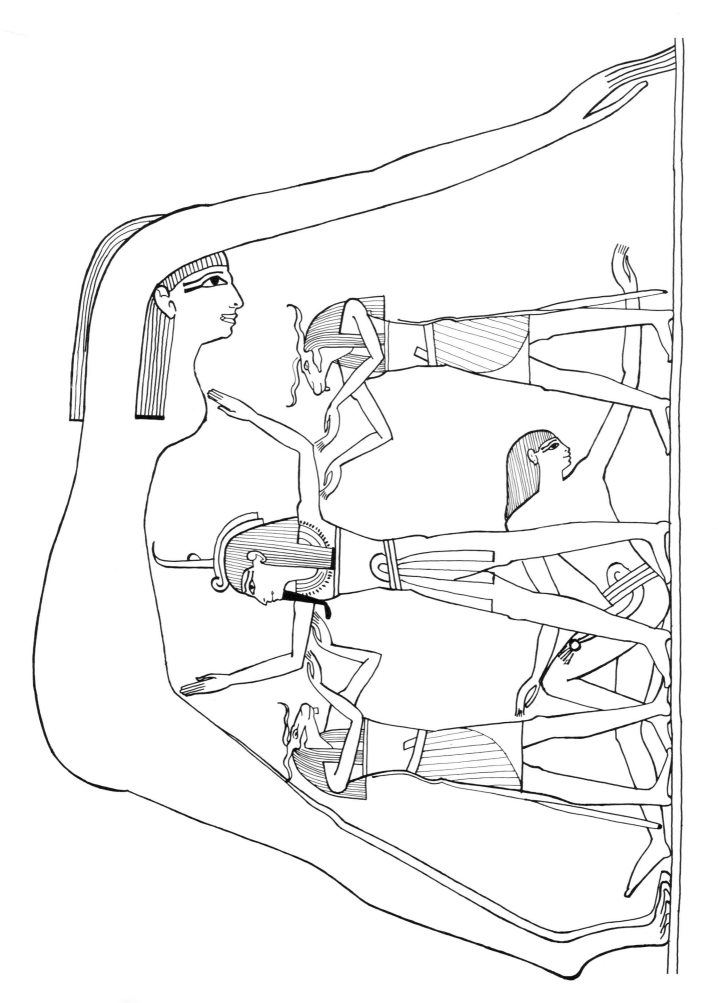

11. Gods and goddesses

The Ancient Egyptians believed that the earth and the sky were full of gods and goddesses. The god of the air, Shu, holds up the goddess of the sky, Nut. The god who is lying down, Geb, is the god of the earth.

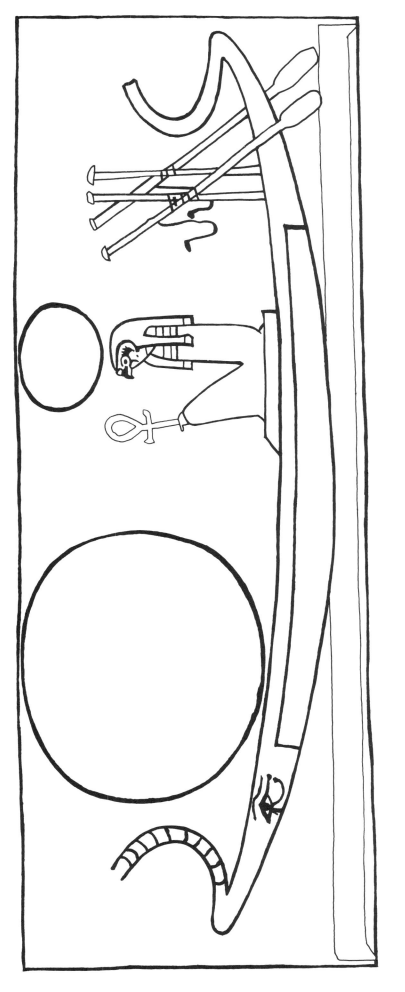

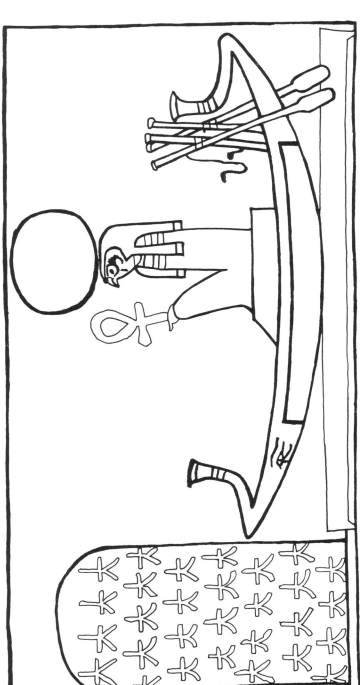

12. Day and night

The Ancient Egyptians believed that the god Ra crossed the sky with the sun in a boat every day (top picture). At night he went under the earth in another boat (bottom picture). He appeared again each morning.

13. The funeral ceremony

It was very important that dead people were treated correctly so that they could live again after death. This is a funeral ceremony outside the tomb. The man's wife is weeping and the god of the dead, Anubis, is taking care of the man's mummified body.

14. Good or bad?

After death each person had to prove that he or she had lived a good life. The god Anubis weighed their heart in the scales of justice. If the heart did not balance it meant the person had been bad and would go to the fierce Eater of the Dead. Good people went on to the afterlife.

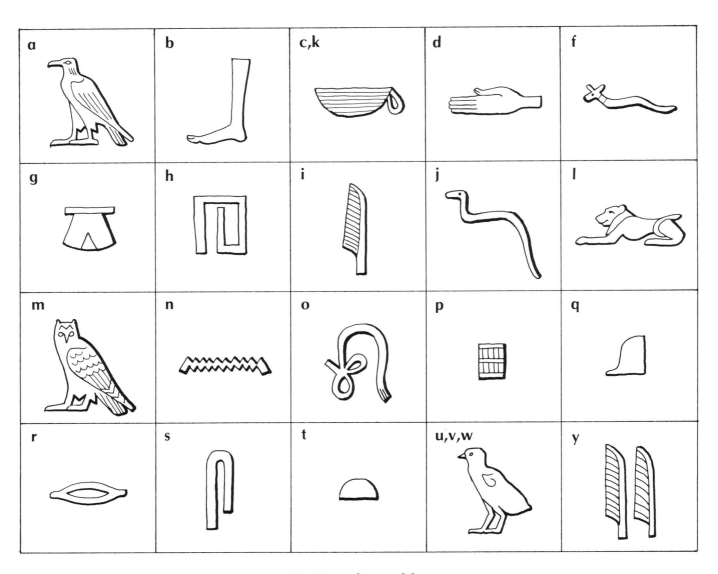

15. Egyptian writing

You have seen lots of Egyptian writing, hieroglyphs, on the other pages of this book. This page shows an 'alphabet' of hieroglyphs. There was no E or X or Z. The letter C was the same as K.

Egyptians put a loop like this, called a cartouche, round important names.

© 1994 The Trustees of the British Museum
Published by British Museum Press
A division of British Museum Publications
46 Bloomsbury Street, London WC1B 3QQ

Reprinted 1996

ISBN 0 7141 0985 1

Drawings by Richard Parkinson

Photoset by Rowland Phototypesetting Ltd
Bury St Edmunds, Suffolk
Printed in Great Britain by
St Edmundsbury Press Ltd, Bury St Edmunds, Suffolk